The Grace Ride

COLORING BOOK

Written by
Kerby Saunders

Illustrated by
Kenneth Lones

Edited by
Leah Saunders

Printed in the United States of America
Published in Hellertown, PA
Illustrations by Kenneth Lones
Library of Congress Control information available upon request
ISBN 978-1-958711-79-8
2 4 6 8 10 9 7 5 3 1

For more information or to place bulk orders, contact the author
or Jennifer@BrightCommunications.net.

Bright
COMMUNICATIONS

BrightCommunications.net

To my wife,

Alice Ballantine

Once upon a time, Timmy, who lived in a small town, wanted a very special super-duper snow sled for Christmas.

Every year, his family
would visit Santa Claus
at the shopping mall.
Timmy could not wait
to see Santa, to ask him
for the super-duper snow sled.

Finally, Timmy got to the mall to see Santa.

He asked Santa for the super-duper snow sled. Santa said that he would talk to his elves to see what he could do.

Timmy was somewhat hopeful he would get the special snow sled on Christmas.

Timmy told his pastor
about the special snow sled
that he wanted for Christmas.

"You also need to ask Jesus
for the special snow sled
because Jesus loves it
when we ask him for things
on his birthday," the pastor said.

Timmy went home that night,
and he got on his knees
by his bed. He asked Jesus
for the super-duper snow sled
for Christmas.

Christmas morning arrived,
and there under
the Christmas tree...

...was the super-duper snow sled!
Timmy jumped for joy to see the
Christmas gift.

It had snowed the night before Christmas. So, now Timmy could go sledding with his very special snow sled.

However, that is not the end
of this Christmas story.

A police report came out
later in the day that the
baby Jesus statue was
missing from the town park.

Everyone was on the lookout
for the missing statue
of the baby Jesus.

When Timmy returned home from sledding, his parents told him that the baby Jesus statue was missing from the park.

Timmy told them that he had
the statue of baby Jesus and
that Jesus was outside
on his sled.

Timmy's parents asked him why he took the statue. They told him that the whole town was upset. Timmy started crying.

Timmy said that he was
so grateful for getting
the super-duper snow sled
that he wanted to take
baby Jesus for a sled ride.

Timmy's parents began to laugh and laugh while Timmy looked at them with confusion.

"You didn't have to take
the statue of the baby Jesus
from the town park for a
sled ride to thank him...,"
Timmy's mom said.

"...because Jesus is
with you wherever you go,"
Timmy's mom said.

"Jesus will never leave you or forget about you," Timmy's mom said.

"We celebrate Christmas
because God so loved the world
that he gave us his son,"
Timmy's mom said.

The End

About the Author

Kerby Saunders lives in Florida with his wife, Alice Ballantine. Kerby has seven children, thirteen grandchildren, and two great-grandchildren. Kerby plays golf, but he especially enjoys playing with his large family.

About the Artist

Kenneth Lones lives in Vero Beach, Florida, with his mom, Carolynn, his dad, Jonathan, and his three siblings, Katherine, Gabe, and Grace. He has been drawing for fun for many years, but The Grace Ride marks the beginning of his career as an illustrator. He is currently studying Digital Media at Indian River State College. Kenneth hopes to eventually write and illustrate books of his own, but until then he's more than happy to bring others' books to life.

About the Editor

Leah Saunders is a longtime fan of the author, children's books, and art. She advised the illustrator on this book. You can find Leah somewhere enjoying life with animals, people, or nature.